Ladybird  Reader

C000059436

Masha and the Bear

Let's Make Dumplings
Activity Book

Based on the
Masha and the Bear TV series

Written by Catrin Morris
Song lyrics on page 16 by Wardour Studios

 Singing *　 Reading　 Speaking　 Critical
thinking

 Spelling　 Writing　 Listening *

1 Find the words. Write the words.

onisdumplingsgornbutterfliesapejarunricaterpillarrpsicutohtpotsec

1 dumplings

2

3

4

5

6

2 Work with a friend.

Ask and answer questions about the picture.

1 Who are they?   They are Masha and Panda.

2 Where are they?   They are . . .

3 What are they doing?   They are . . .

4 What color is Panda?   He is . . .

3

3 Look and read. Circle the correct words.

1  Panda was **angry.** /(**hungry.**) He wanted to make dumplings.

2  Masha could not catch the caterpillar. It was too **quick.** / **slow.**

3  The caterpillar and Masha ran on the table. Panda was not **happy.** / **sad.**

4  Masha played with the dough. "This is **boring!"** / **fun!"** said Masha.

5  Panda made **big** / **small** and **beautiful** / **ugly** dumplings.

6  Masha made **big** / **small** and **beautiful** / **ugly** dumplings!

4 **Look and read. Choose the correct words and write them on the lines.** 📖 ✏️ ❓

dumplings   caterpillar   dough

butterflies   jar   pot

1 You can eat .... *dumplings* ....

2 You make dumplings with ....

3 Masha wants to catch a ....

4 You can cook dumplings in a ....

5 Caterpillars change into ....

6 Masha puts the caterpillar in a ....

5 Listen, and complete the sentences.
Where are these things? 🎧* ✏️

1 Masha

She is behind the
_____caterpillar_____ .

2 caterpillar

It is in the
....

3 dough

It is in front of Masha's
....

4 hats

They are on
Panda and Bear's
....

5 dumplings

They are in the
....

6 pot

It is under the
....

*To complete this activity, listen to track 2 of the Reader audio download available at www.ladybirdeducation.co.uk

6

Look at the pictures.
Put a ✓ **in the correct boxes.**

1

a cat ☐
b cut ✓

2

a doe ☐
b dough ☐

3

a role ☐
b roll ☐

4

a ja ☐
b jar ☐

5

a pot ☐
b put ☐

6

a Bare ☐
b Bear ☐

7 Read, and circle the correct words.

1  Bear and Panda **was** / **were** in the kitchen. They **wants** / **wanted** to make dumplings.

2  First, they **got** / **gets** some dough.

3  Panda **roll** / **rolled** the dough.

4  Bear cut the dough and **make** / **made** balls with it.

8

Look at the pictures. Which picture is different? Put a ✓ in the correct boxes and write the sentences below. 📖 ✏️ ❓

| She is not helping. | It is not there. |
| It is big and ugly. | They are happy. |

1

 a  b  c

She is not helping.

2

a  b  c

3

a   b  c

4

a  b  c

9 Write *What* or *Where*.

1 ___Where___ is Panda?

He is in the kitchen.

2 _____ is he doing?

He is making dumplings.

3 _____ is Masha?

She is on the table.

4 _____ does she want to do?

She wants to catch a caterpillar.

5 _____ is the dough?

It is on the table, too.

10 **Look and read. Write short answers.**

1

Does Masha catch the caterpillar?

Yes, she does.

2

Is Panda happy?

....

3

Are Panda's dumplings beautiful?

....

4

Are Masha's dumplings beautiful?

....

5

Where do the butterflies come from?

....

11 Listen, and write a—f.

Masha was outside. She wanted to catch butterflies.

Then, she saw a caterpillar. "Hello, little caterpillar! You can be my friend!" she said.

She could not catch the caterpillar. It was too quick.

12

13

1 Then, she saw a caterpillar. ....C............

2 Masha was outside. ....

3 "Hello, little caterpillar!" ....

4 She could not catch the caterpillar.
    It was too quick. ....

5 "You can be my friend!" she said. ....

6 She wanted to catch butterflies. ....

*To complete this activity, listen to track 3 of the Reader audio download available at **www.ladybirdeducation.co.uk**

12 **Work with a friend. Help Masha catch the caterpillar. Use the words in the box.**

turn right   go straight   turn left   go to the end

Turn right. Then, turn left . . .

13 **Circle the correct pictures.** ?

1 Who cuts the dough?

2 What does Masha catch?

3 Who is angry?

4 Who makes beautiful dumplings?

5 Which dumplings are small?

Look, and match the two parts of the words.

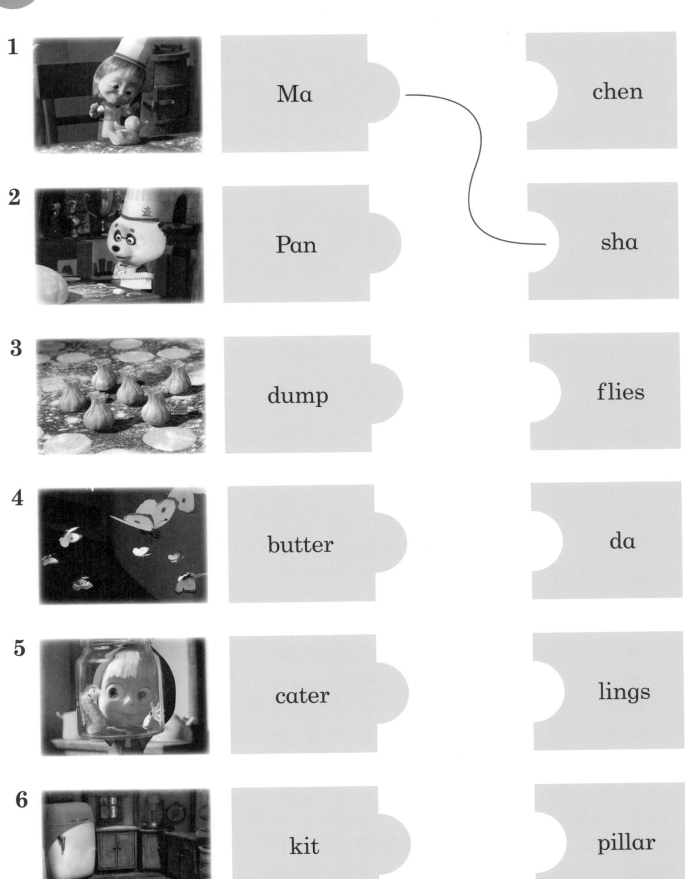

1   Ma   chen

2   Pan   sha

3   dump   flies

4   butter   da

5   cater   lings

6   kit   pillar

15 **Sing the song.** *

Let's make dumplings, let's make dumplings.
Roll the dough, roll the dough.
Let's make dumplings, let's make dumplings.
Cut the dough and make balls with it!

I want to play with the dough! Ooh, ooh, ooh!
I want to make dumplings, too!
Make a bird, or a face, or sausages.
Ha ha ha, what fun this is!

Let's make dumplings, let's make dumplings.
Roll the dough, roll the dough.
Let's make dumplings, let's make dumplings.
Cut the dough and make balls with it!

Panda made dumplings, small and beautiful.
Masha and the caterpillar ran on the table.
Bear looked in the pot, what did he find?
Lots and lots of butterflies!

Let's make dumplings, let's make dumplings.
Roll the dough, roll the dough.
Let's make dumplings, let's make dumplings
Cut the dough and make balls with it!

 *To complete this activity, listen to track 4 of the Reader audio download available at www.ladybirdeducation.co.uk